Tales of Oaktree Wood

# SPINDLE'S PICNIC

by Rene Cloke

AWARD PUBLICATIONS LIMITED

Spindle Hedgehog lived in a
cosy little house in the root of
a tree on the edge of Oaktree Wood.
"It's a fine sunny day," he said, looking out of
the door one morning, "I'll take a picnic
down to the river."

He cut some sandwiches,
packed some cheese and biscuits
and an orange.

"I think that will be enough,"
he decided.

Spindle put the packet into the carrier
of his bicycle, put on his jacket and scarf
and rode off through the woods
towards the river.

"A lovely day for a ride." called Mandy Mouse as he rode past her house, "Have a good time."

Then he met Filbert and Sally Squirrel
who were looking very worried.

"We've lost little Frisky," they told him, "he didn't
come home yesterday evening and he has been
out all night."

"I hope he hasn't fallen into the river," said Sally,
"he hasn't yet learnt how to swim."

"I'm going down to the river,"
Spindle told them, "I'll keep
a sharp look-out for him.
I expect he has lost his way
in the woods."

When Spindle reached
the river, he propped his
bicycle against a tree
and went down to the
water's edge.

"How cool and fresh the water looks," he said,
"I think I'll have a paddle before I eat my lunch."

He wandered up the river and on his way back
saw Winnie Water-vole carrying a heavy basket
on her way home from the woodland shop.

"Oh, dear! How tired I am!" she sighed.

"Would you like to borrow my bicycle?"
suggested Spindle. "You could hang your basket
on the handlebar. I don't mind walking home."

Winnie was very grateful
and rode off on Spindle's bicycle
with her shopping.

The hedgehog sat in the sun
to dry his feet and then he thought
about his lunch.

"Oh, how stupid I am!" he cried, "I've left my picnic lunch in the carrier of my bicycle."

Then he thought hard.

"I'd better walk along through the woods to the shop and see what I can buy; I'm afraid I haven't much money in my pocket."

Spindle put on his jacket and his shoes and socks and walked off through the trees to the little shop kept by Belinda Bunny.

He felt very hungry and bought a pie and an apple.

There were a great many people in the shop
and Spindle asked if any of them had seen
little Frisky Squirrel.
Everyone said "No," but promised to look out for him.

As Spindle walked back
to the river he heard
a little squeak and there,
in the rushes, with his foot caught
between two rocks, was little Frisky
looking very wet and uncomfortable.

"Help! help!" he cried,
"I can't get my foot free!
I crawled along that branch
to pick some nuts
and I fell off into the river
and got caught in the
rocks."

Spindle put down his bag of shopping, took off his jacket and his shoes and socks and waded into the river.

"I'm coming," he called out to Frisky.

He soon reached the little squirrel
and managed to move the big stone
and get the foot free.

Together they waded back to the shore
and sat down on the grass to dry their
wet feet and legs.

"I'm so hungry," whimpered the little squirrel,
"I lost my way in the woods when it got dark
and I didn't have any supper last night or any
breakfast this morning. I don't know what
time it is but I don't think I'll have
any lunch today."

Spindle looked at his pie and his apple.

He was hungry, too, but he was a kind
little hedgehog and gave the pie to Frisky
and took just one bite from the apple.
Charlie Chaffinch hoped that
there might be something for him.

"Now we must hurry home," said Spindle, when Frisky had eaten every crumb, "it is getting dark and everyone is very worried about you."

Frisky was so tired that Spindle offered to carry him on his back, but the hedgehog was so covered with spines that Frisky found it wasn't very comfortable.

Filbert and Sally
were delighted to
see them and young Frisky
had a long story
to tell about his
adventures.

"But first of all,"
declared Sally, "you must
both come in and have
a good meal.
Tea is ready!"

Oh, it was a lovely tea!
There was a big dish of eggs and mushrooms,
plenty of cakes, bread and butter and a
lovely apple pie with cream.

All the squirrel family gathered round
the table and Spindle and Frisky were given
big helpings of everything until they
simply couldn't eat any more!

Then they sat around the fire and Frisky
told them all about his wanderings in the
dark woods last night and about the way Spindle
had rescued him from the river and
given him his pie and his apple.

At last, Spindle said "Goodnight," waved goodbye to the squirrels and hurried home.

"Well," he murmured as he crept into bed, "I didn't have my picnic sandwiches and I didn't have my pie but that lovely tea made up for missing them!" and he fell asleep dreaming about rescuing little squirrels and apples and oranges from the river.

Next day there was a surprise present for him on the doorstep.

A big basket of fruit from Filbert and Sally with a little note to thank him for his kindness to young Frisky.